Jigs, Reels & Hornpipes

TRADITIONAL FIDDLE TUNES FROM ENGLAND, IRELAND & SCOTLAND

TRADITIONELLE FIDEL-MELODIEN AUS ENGLAND, IRLAND UND SCHOTTLAND · DANSES TRADITIONNELLES D'ANGLETERRE, D'IRLANDE ET D'ECOSSE

Selected and arranged by EDWARD HUWS JONES

BOOSEY & HAWKES

Boosey & Hawkes Music Publishers Ltd

www.boosey.com

Preface

The traditional music of England, Scotland and Ireland is a wonderful and almost limitless source of music for the violin. These melodies, an essential part of our musical heritage, offer an irresistible repertoire for violin players of all standards, young and old.

One of the ideas behind this collection is to give players the chance to really let their hair down and create music which has instant appeal and razzmatazz. These arrangements bring a fresh note to all sorts of performances, formal or informal, indoors or out.

Jigs, Reels & Hornpipes is a very flexible resource, and can be used in lots of different ways according to the instruments and players available. The violin melody can be played with the other parts in any combination, as duets, trios or larger ensembles. The easy violin part can readily be transcribed for flute (playing up an octave) or clarinet. Adding rhythm guitar, bass guitar and drums transforms the ensemble into an electric folk band. Or the tunes can be played simply as solos with piano accompaniment.

With thousands of traditional fiddle tunes to choose from, the selection of music for *Jigs, Reels & Hornpipes* was almost impossible. These thirty tunes are some of my personal favourites, are also accessible to student violinists and work well in this kind of arrangement. I hope this collection will whet appetites for the larger repertoire found in the standard anthologies of traditional fiddle music.

Much of the character of traditional fiddle music, its subtle nuances, cannot be captured on the page. However, the energy and enjoyment that enthusiastic players bring to this music is truly 'authentic' and in the best fiddle tradition.

Edward Huws Jones

Vorwort

Die ursprüngliche Musik Englands, Schottlands und Irlands ist eine wundervolle und fast unerschöpfliche Quelle an Musik für Geige. Diese Melodien, die einen grundlegenden Teil unseres musikalischen Erbes darstellen, bieten ein unwiderstehliches Repertoire für Geiger aller Lernstufen – ob jung oder alt.

Eine der Ideen, die hinter dieser Sammlung steht, ist, dem Spieler Gelegenheit zu geben, völlig aus sich herauszugehen und Musik zu schaffen, die animiert und Spaß macht. Diese Arrangements geben jeder Vorstellung, ob formal oder locker, drinnen oder draußen, eine frische Note.

Jigs, Reels & Hornpipes ist eine vielseitige Quelle und kann auf viele verschiedene Weisen gespielt werden – abgestimmt auf die verfügbaren Instrumente und Spieler. Die Geigenstimme kann mit den anderen Stimmen in jeder Zusammensetzung gespielt werden – als Duett, Trio oder im größeren Ensemble. Die vereinfachte Violinstimme kann ohne weiteres für Flöte (eine Oktave höher) oder Klarinette umgeschrieben werden. Nimmt man Rhythmische Gitarre, Baßgitarre und Schlagzeug hinzu, wird das Ensemble zur 'Electric Folk Band'. Genauso gut können die Melodien ganz einfach als Solo mit Klavierbegleitung gespielt werden.

Bei Tausenden von überlieferten Fidel-Melodien war es fast unmöglich, eine Titelauswahl für *Jigs, Reels & Hornpipes* zu treffen. Diese 30 Stücke gehören zu meinen Lieblingsmelodien. Sie sind auch für Geigenanfänger zugänglich und passen gut in diese Art von Arrangement. Ich hoffe, diese Sammlung wird die Neugierde auf den wesentlich größeren Fundus an Standard-Anthologien traditioneller Fidel-Musik wecken.

Vom Charakter ursprünglicher Fidel-Musik und ihrer feinen Nuancen konnte nicht viel in dieser kurzen Einführung eingefangen werden. Aber wie auch immer – die Energie und die Freude, die begeisterte Spieler dieser Musik entgegenbringen, ist wirklich 'authentisch' und folgt der besten Fidel-Tradition.

Edward Huws Jones

Préface

La musique traditionnelle de l'Angleterre, de l'Ecosse et de l'Irlande est une source merveilleuse et pratiquement illimitée de musique pour le violon. Ces mélodies sont une partie essentielle de notre héritage musical et constituent un répertoire irrésistible pour les violonistes de tous niveaux, les jeunes comme les moins jeunes.

Un des buts de cette collection est de donner au musicien la possibilité de se laisser aller et de créer une musique au charme et à l'entrain immédiats. Ces arrangements apportent une note fraîche à toutes sortes d'occasions musicales, en public ou entre amis, en salle comme en plein air.

Jigs, Reels & Hornpipes offre des ressources extrêmement variées qui peuvent s'utiliser de toutes sortes de façons différentes selon les musiciens et les instruments dont on dispose. La mélodie de violon peut se jouer en combinaison avec n'importe quelle autre partie pour former des duos, des trios ou des ensembles plus importants. La partie d'accompagnement facile pour le violon peut aussi être jouée par la flûte (transposée à l'octave supérieure) ou par la clarinette. En ajoutant guitare rythmique, guitare basse et percussion, on transforme l'ensemble en une formation de musique folk électrique. Les airs peuvent aussi être interprétés simplement en solo avec accompagnement de piano.

Avec des milliers d'airs traditionnels parmi lesquels choisir, il fut pratiquement impossible de sélectionner la musique pour *Jigs, Reels & Hornpipes*. Ces trente morceaux comptent parmi mes favoris; ils sont à la portée de ceux qui apprennent le violon, et se prêtent bien à ce type d'arrangement. J'espère que cette collection mettra les musiciens en appétit pour le riche répertoire qui se trouve dans les principales anthologies de musique traditionnelle pour le violon.

Ce qui constitue l'esprit de la musique traditionnelle pour le violon, ses nuances subtiles, ne peut pas vraiment se reproduire dans ces pages. Quoi qu'il en soit, l'énergie et la joie que les joueurs enthousiastes apportent à cette musique sont véritablement 'authentiques' et sont dans la meilleure tradition du violon populaire.

Edward Huws Jones

For Rob Thomson, Fiona Goodwill
and the Millthorpe School Fiddle Band, York

Cover illustration by Peter Bailey
Layout by Sue Clarke

Contents

ENGLAND
Hunting the Hare

JIG

The Fairy Dance

REEL

Morpeth Rant

HORNPIPE

Constant Billy

MORRIS DANCE

The Keel Row

6

Country Gardens

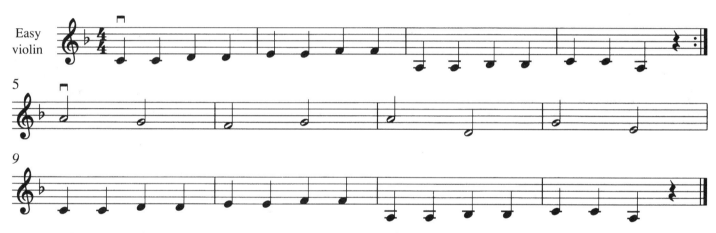

The Staffordshire Hornpipe

HORNPIPE

The Girl I Left Behind Me

MARCH

King of the Fairies

HORNPIPE

The Trumpet Hornpipe

IRELAND

The Wind that Shakes the Barley

REEL

The Bridal

JIG

D.C. al Fine

D.C. al Fine

Danny Boy

The Peeler's Away with My Daughter

JIG

Violin melody

Easy violin

Red-Haired Boy

The Fox Hunter's Jig

SLIP JIG

Drowsy Maggie

Harvest Home

HORNPIPE

Carolan's Air

The Mason's Apron

REEL

SCOTLAND
The Bonny Lass o' Fyvie

BOTHY BALLAD

Brochan Lom

STRATHSPEY

Mrs Jamieson's Favourite

Charles Grant
AIR

Lord MacDonald's Reel

REEL

The Flowers of Edinburgh

REEL

Miss Sally Hunter of Thurston

Nathaniel Gow
JIG

Mary, Young and Fair

AIR

The Gay Gordons

The Spey in Spate

James Scott Skinner
REEL

Earl Grey

STRATHSPEY

Reproduced and printed by
Halstan & Co. Ltd., Amersham, Bucks., England